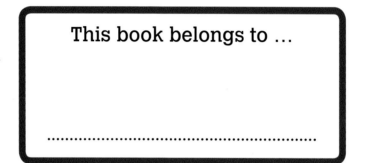

This book belongs to ...

....

OXFORD
UNIVERSITY PRESS

Great Clarendon Street, Oxford, OX2 6DP,
United Kingdom

Oxford University Press is a department of the University of Oxford.
It furthers the University's objective of excellence in research, scholarship,
and education by publishing worldwide. Oxford is a registered trade mark of
Oxford University Press in the UK and in certain other countries

Acknowledgements;
Series Editors: Kate Ruttle, Annemarie Young

READ WITH
Biff,
Chip &
Kipper

The Moon Jet
and Other Stories

OXFORD
UNIVERSITY PRESS

Tips for Reading Together

Children learn best when reading is fun.

- Talk about the title and the picture on the cover.
- Identify the letter pattern *oo* in the title and talk about the sound it makes when you read it.
- Look at the *oo* words on page 8. Say the sounds in each word and then say the word (e.g. *m-oo-n, moon*).
- Read the story and find the words with *oo*.
- Do the fun learning activity at the end of the book.

Children enjoy re-reading stories and this helps to build their confidence.

Have fun!

After you have read the story, find Little Ted in eight of the pictures.

The main sound practised in this book is 'oo' as in *soon*.

For more hints and tips on helping your child become a successful and enthusiatic reader look at our website www.oxfordowl.co.uk.

The Moon Jet

Written by Roderick Hunt
Illustrated by Nick Schon,
based on the original characters
created by Roderick Hunt and Alex Brychta

OXFORD
UNIVERSITY PRESS

7

Read these words

moon   soon

cool   shoot

zoom   shoo

boom   food

Kipper had a box and a bin.

Kipper got in his jet . . .

. . . and put on the lid.

"This jet is cool," said Kipper.

"Off I go," he said.

boom

boom

The jet shot off.

It shot out of the room.

"I will loop the loop,"
said Kipper.

The jet did six loops.

"I will go to the moon,"
said Kipper.

"I can get to it soon,"
he said.

The jet got to the moon.

But the moon bugs ran up.

"Yuk," said Kipper.

"Moon bugs."

"Shoo, get off," said Kipper.

"Did I nod off?" said Kipper.

"Yes," said Mum. "Get up to bed."

Talk about the story

Where did Kipper go in his jet?

What happened when he got there?

How did Kipper make his jet?

Where would you go if you had a jet?

25

A maze

Help Kipper to get to the moon.

Tips for Reading Together

Children learn best when reading is fun.

- Talk about the title and the picture on page 29.
- Identify the letter pattern *qu* in the title and talk about the sound it makes when you read it.
- Look at the *qu*, *ou* and *ck* words on page 30. Say the sounds in each word and then say the word (e.g. *qu-i-ck*, *quick*; *ou-t*, *out*).
- Read the story then find the words with *qu*, *ou* and *ck*.
- Talk about the story and do the fun activity at the end of the book.

Children enjoy re-reading stories and this helps to build their confidence.

Have fun!

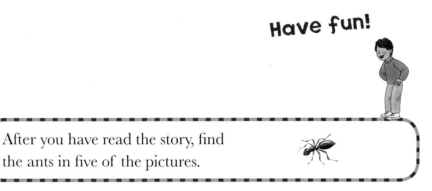

After you have read the story, find the ants in five of the pictures.

The main sounds practised in this book are 'qu' as in *quick*, and 'ou' as in *out*. The other sound practised is 'ck' as in *quick*.

For more hints and tips on helping your child become a successful and enthusiatic reader look at our website www.oxfordowl.co.uk.

Quick! Quick!

Written by Roderick Hunt
Illustrated by Nick Schon,
based on the original characters
created by Roderick Hunt and Alex Brychta

OXFORD
UNIVERSITY PRESS

Read these words

quick   out

ouch   stuck

stick   jack

The ball shot off.

"I can get it," said Kipper.

But Kipper got stuck.

Biff ran to get Dad.

Quick, quick.

"Kipper is stuck," said Biff.

"I can get him out," said Dad.

"He is still stuck," said Biff.

Dad rang Mum.

Quick, quick.

"Kipper is stuck," said Dad.

Mum got a big stick.

"Ouch," said Kipper. "I am still stuck."

Wilma ran to get her dad.

"Kipper is stuck," said Wilma.

Wilma's dad got his jack.

This jack will get him out.

Kipper got out.

Dad was stuck.

Talk about the story

How did Kipper get stuck?

What did Wilma's dad use to get Kipper out?

Why did Dad get stuck?

Have you got stuck before? Where?

A maze

Help Kipper get the ball.

Tips for Reading Together

Children learn best when reading is fun.

- Talk about the title and the picture on page 51.
- Discuss what you think the story might be about.
- Read the story together, inviting your child to read with you.
- Give lots of praise as your child reads with you, and help them when necessary.
- If they get stuck, read the first sound or syllable of the word, or read the whole sentence. Focus on the meaning.
- Re-read the story later, encouraging your child to read as much of it as they can.

Children enjoy re-reading stories and this helps to build their confidence.

Have fun!

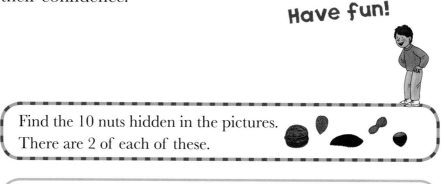

Find the 10 nuts hidden in the pictures.
There are 2 of each of these.

This book includes these useful common words:
said   was   saw   looked

For more hints and tips on helping your child become a successful and enthusiastic reader look at our website www.oxfordowl.co.uk.

50

Missing!

Written by Roderick Hunt
Illustrated by Alex Brychta

OXFORD
UNIVERSITY PRESS

Nadim had a hamster.

He called it Jaws.

"Jaws is a funny name for
a hamster," said Biff.

Nadim put Jaws in his cage, but
he forgot to shut the cage door.

Jaws got out of the cage and
ran off.

Nadim saw the cage was open.

"Oh no!" he said.

Nadim was upset.

"Jaws has run off," said Nadim.

"We can look for him," said Biff.

They looked and looked.

Biff looked under the sink.

Chip looked in the fridge.

Nadim looked under the
cupboard.

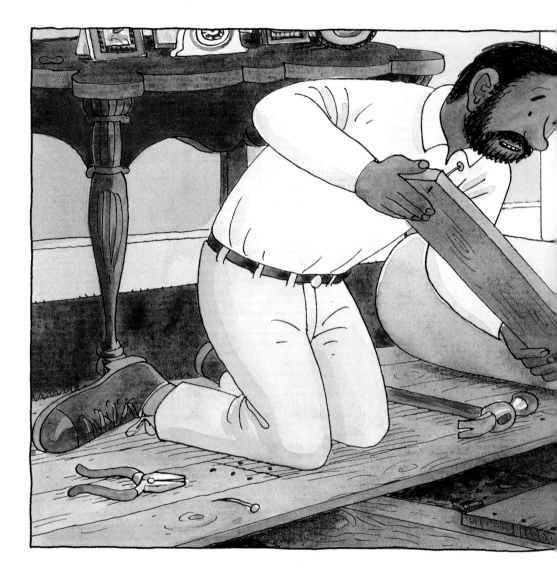

Nadim's dad looked under
the floor.

"Is Jaws down here?" he said.

Then Chip had an idea.

"Let's get Floppy. He can help us."

Sniff, sniff, went Floppy.

Sniff, sniff! SNIFF! SNIFF!

"Look in there," said Chip.

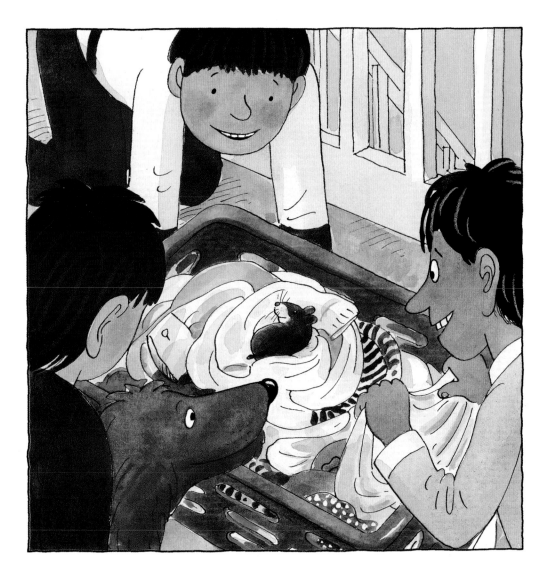

Jaws was in the clothes basket.

He had made a nest.

"Look!" said Nadim. "You can see why I called him Jaws."

Talk about the story

Why is the hamster called Jaws?

Why was Nadim upset when he found that Jaws had run away?

Where did the children and Dad look for Jaws?

What would you do if you lost your pet?

Odd one out

Which two things don't begin with the same sound as the 'h' at the beginning of 'hamster'?

Tips for Reading Together

Children learn best when reading is fun.

- Talk about the title and the picture on page 73.
- Discuss what you think the story might be about.
- Read the story together, inviting your child to read with you.
- Give lots of praise as your child reads with you, and help them when necessary.
- If they get stuck, read the first sound or syllable of the word, or read the whole sentence. Focus on the meaning.
- Re-read the story later, encouraging your child to read as much of it as they can.

Children enjoy re-reading stories and this helps to build their confidence.

Have fun!

After you have read the story, find the 3 dragonflies, 3 frogs, 3 fish and 3 newts hidden in the pictures.

This book includes these useful common words:
said   children   went   going

For more hints and tips on helping your child become a successful and enthusiastic reader look at our website www.oxfordowl.co.uk.

The Raft Race

Written by Roderick Hunt
Illustrated by Alex Brychta

OXFORD
UNIVERSITY PRESS

The children were at the river.

It was raft race day.

Mum and Dad made a raft.

The children helped.

"This is a good raft," said Dad.

"Let's get it into the water."

They slid the raft into the water.
Dad pulled it. Wilma and Chip
pushed.

Mum and Dad got on.

"Don't fall in," said Wilf.

The raft race started. Mum and
Dad went fast.

"Go! Go! Go!" shouted Biff.

"You can win."

Mum and Dad went faster.
"Come on!" puffed Dad. "We
can win."

Oh no! The raft broke.

SPLASH! Dad fell in the water.

"Go on, Mum," shouted Wilf.

"You can still win."

Mum kept going.

Dad got back on his raft.

"Go on, Dad," shouted Wilma.

"Go as fast as you can."

Oh no! The raft broke again.

SPLASH! Dad fell in the water.

Mum kept going and she
won the race!

"Good old Mum," said Wilma.

"Poor old Dad," said Wilf.

Talk about the story

Why did the raft break in half?

What did Dad do after the raft broke?

The children were pleased for Mum. How did they feel about Dad?

Have you ever been in a boat or on a raft? What would you do if you fell in?

Find the pairs

Each set of creatures has an odd one out.
Can you find each one?

Read with Biff, Chip and Kipper
The UK's best-selling home reading series

Phonics

First Stories

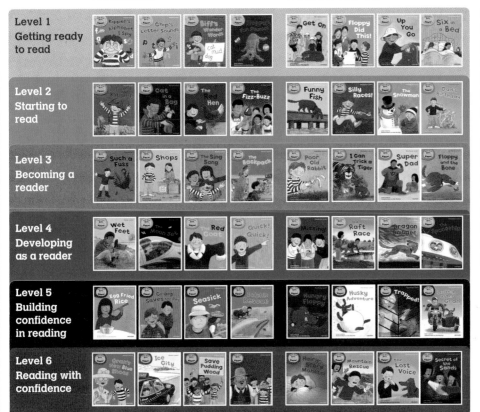

	Phonics	First Stories
Level 1 Getting ready to read	Kipper's Alphabet I Spy · Chip's Letter Sounds · Biff's Wonder Words	Get On · Floppy Did This! · Up You Go · Six in a Bed
Level 2 Starting to read	Cat in a Bag · The Red Hen · The Fizz-Buzz	Funny Fish · Silly Races! · The Snowman · Dad's Birthday
Level 3 Becoming a reader	Such a Fuss · Shops · The Sing Song · The Backpack	Poor Old Rabbit · I Can Trick a Tiger · Super Dad · Floppy and the Bone
Level 4 Developing as a reader	Wet Feet · The Moon Jet · Red · Quick! Quick!	Missing · Raft Race · Dragon Danger · The Spaceship
Level 5 Building confidence in reading	Egg Fried Rice · Craig Saves · Seasick · Bertha Rescue	Hungry Floppy · Husky Adventure · Trapped!
Level 6 Reading with confidence	Gran's New Blue Shoes · Ice City · Save Pudding Wood	Hairy Scary Monster · Mountain Rescue · The Lost Voice · Secret of the Sands

Phonics stories help children practise their sounds and letters, as they learn to do in school.

First Stories have been specially written to provide practice in reading everyday language.

Read with Biff, Chip and Kipper Collections:

 Up You Go and Other Stories

 Six in a Bed and Other Stories

 Funny Fish and Other Stories

The Fizz-Buzz

 Floppy and the Bone and Other Stories

I Can Trick a Tiger

 The Moon Jet and Other Stories

 Dragon Danger

 2 Phonics and 2 First Stories in every collection

Phonics support

Flashcards are a really fun way to practise phonics and build reading skills. **Age 3+**

My Phonics Kit is designed to support you and your child as you practise phonics together at home. It includes stickers, workbooks, interactive eBooks, support for parents and more! **Age 5+**

Read Write Inc. Phonics: A range of fun rhyming stories to support decoding skills. **Age 4+**

Songbirds Phonics: Lively and engaging phonics stories from Children's Laureate, Julia Donaldson. **Age 4+**

Help your child's reading with essential tips, advice on phonics and free eBooks
www.oxfordowl.co.uk